USBORNE KE...

Practice
Times Tables

Written by Sam Smith

Illustrated by Marta Cabrol

Designed by Laura Hammonds,
Winsome d'Abreu and
Carly Davies

Series Editor: Felicity Brooks

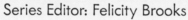

$6 \times 2 = 12$

Once you've completed an activity page in this book,
you can check it using the answer pages at the back.

Groups of 3

This group of 3 monkeys is having fun around the tree. Trace over the numbers in the boxes to finish the sentence.

1 group of 3 monkeys = 3 monkeys altogether.

3 6 9 12 15 18 21 24 27 30

These groups of 3 bears are paddling their canoes on the river. Count the groups, then write the numbers in the boxes to finish the sentence.

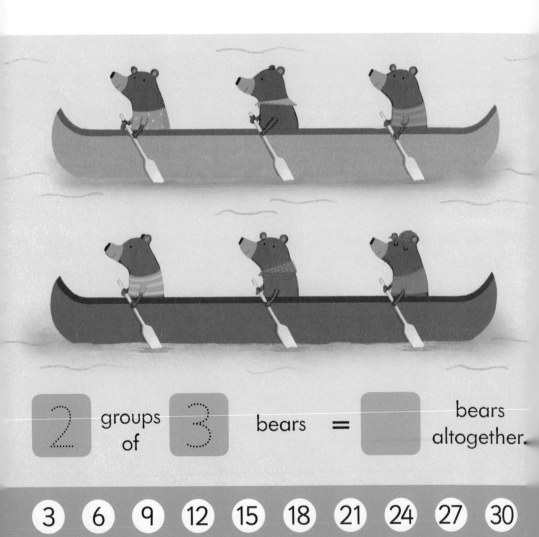

2 groups of 3 bears = ☐ bears altogether.

3 6 9 12 15 18 21 24 27 30

Adding in threes

Help Tig add up these numbers.
Write the totals in the boxes.

$3 + 3 + 3 + 3 + 3 + 3 + 3 + 3 =$ ☐

$3 + 3 + 3 + 3 + 3 =$ ☐

Hold steady,
Crock!

$3 + 3 + 3 =$ ☐

$3 + 3 + 3 + 3 =$ ☐

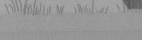

(3) (6) (9) (12) (15) (18) (21) (24) (27) (30)

Groups of 3

4

These lily pads grow in groups of 3 on the river.
Count the groups, then write the numbers
in the boxes to finish the sentence.

3 groups of 3 lily pads = ☐ lily pads altogether.

3 6 9 12 15 18 21 24 27 30

Groups of 3

These lily pads grow in groups of 3.
Count the groups, then write the numbers
in the boxes to finish the sentence.

4 groups of 3 lily pads = ☐ lily pads altogether.

3 6 9 12 15 18 21 24 27 30

Flower threes

Help Lem count the flowers in threes. Follow the arrows, and write the new total under each group.

3 → 6 → ☐ → ☐

☐ ← ☐ ← ☐ ← ☐

☐ → ☐

I know the numbers will alternate between odd and even.

Honeycomb

Find a route across the honeycomb. The next cell's number must always be 3 more than the number of the cell you are on.

Start

14 17

5 9 11 16 20

3 8 10 13 19 23 25

6 12 16 17 21 26

10 9 15 18 22 24 27

18 23 22 21 24 28

20 21 24 25 26 27 31

26 27 28 29 30

29 32

Finish

Groups of 3

These parrots are perching in groups of 3.
Count the groups, then write the numbers
in the boxes to finish the sentence.

| | groups of | 3 | parrots = | | parrots altogether. |

 3 6 9  12 15 18 21 24 27 30

Groups of 3

These parrots are perching in groups of 3.
Count the groups, then write the numbers
in the boxes to finish the sentence.

☐ groups of **3** parrots = ☐ parrots altogether.

③ ⑥ ⑨ ⑫ ⑮ ⑱ ㉑ ㉔ ㉗ ㉚

Sequences

Fill in the missing numbers in these sequences so that each number is 3 more than the one before.

3   6   9   12

18   27

6   15

12

Groups of 3

These leopard cubs all have 3 spots on their fur.
Count the cubs, then write the numbers in
the boxes to finish the sentence.

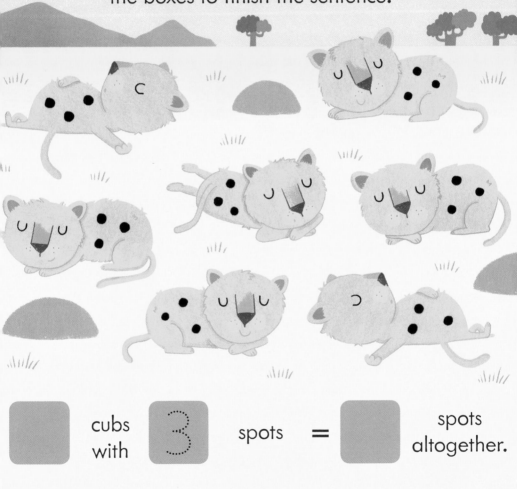

☐ cubs with **3** spots = ☐ spots altogether.

3 6 9 12 15 18 21 24 27 30

Groups of 3

These leopard cubs all have 3 spots.
Count the cubs, then write the numbers
in the boxes to finish the sentence.

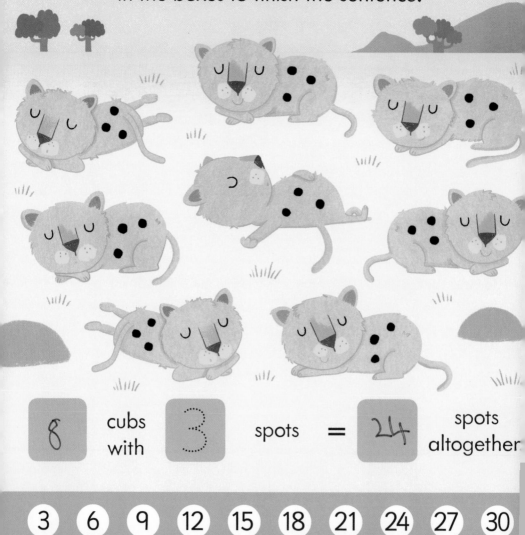

8 cubs with 3 spots = 24 spots altogether

3 6 9 12 15 18 21 24 27 30

Sequences

Fill in the missing numbers in these sequences so that each number is 3 more than the one before.

9 ⬜ ⬜ 18

15 ⬜ ⬜ ⬜

⬜ ⬜ 9 ⬜

21 ⬜ ⬜ ⬜

Groups of 3

These tiger cubs all have 3 stripes on their fur.
Count the cubs, then write the numbers in
the boxes to finish the sentence.

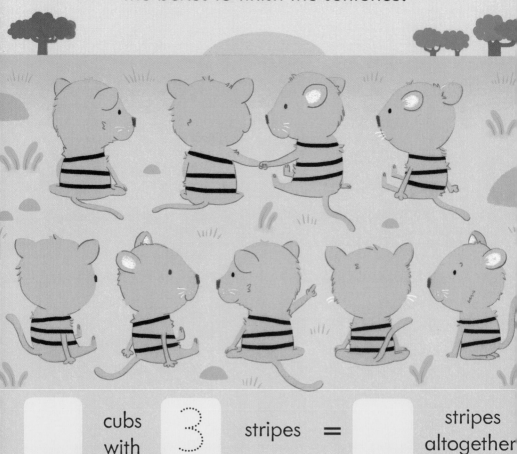

☐ cubs with 3 stripes = ☐ stripes altogether

3   6   9   12   15   18   21   24   27   30

Groups of 3

These tiger cubs all have 3 stripes.
Count the cubs, then write the numbers
in the boxes to finish the sentence.

☐ cubs with ⋮3⋮ stripes = ☐ stripes altogether.

(3) (6) (9) (12) (15) (18) (21) (24) (27) (30)

3 times table

Trace over the dotted numbers and fill in the empty boxes to finish these calculations in the 3 times table.

1 × 3 = ⬜   6 × 3 = ⬜

2 × 3 = ⬜   7 × 3 = ⬜

3 × 3 = ⬜   8 × 3 = ⬜

4 × 3 = ⬜   9 × 3 = ⬜

5 × 3 = ⬜   10 × 3 = ⬜

Calculation pairs

Lep and Baz have been picking oranges. Fill in the numbers in the calculations below to see how many oranges they each have, and to see if Baz is right.

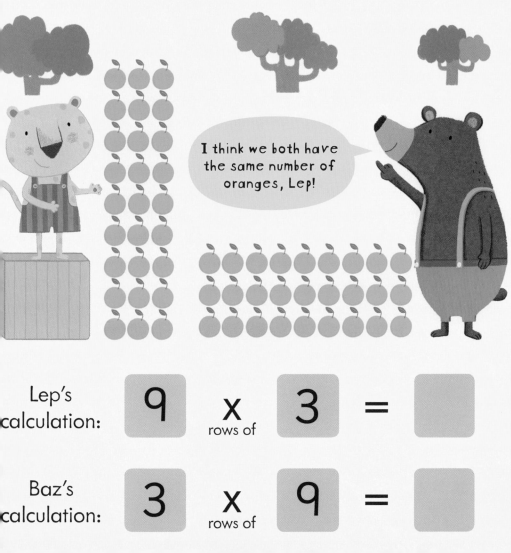

I think we both have the same number of oranges, Lep!

Lep's calculation:

$$9 \quad \times \quad 3 \quad = \quad \boxed{}$$

rows of

Baz's calculation:

$$3 \quad \times \quad 9 \quad = \quad \boxed{}$$

rows of

3 groups

These mice are in 3 groups. Count how
many mice are in each group, then
write the numbers in the boxes.

$$3 \times \boxed{} = \boxed{}$$

3 6 9 12 15 18 21 24 27 30

3 groups

These bugs are in 3 groups. Count how many bugs are in each group, then write the numbers in the boxes.

3 × ☐ = ☐

3 6 9 12 15 18 21 24 27 30

Calculation pairs

Fill in the spaces to complete two different calculations for each group of fish. One has been done for you.

$3 \times 2 = 6$
$2 \times 3 = 6$

...... $\times 3 =$ ......
...... $\times 8 =$ ......

$3 \times$ ...... $=$ ......
$6 \times$ ...... $=$ ......

Calculation pairs

Fill in the spaces to complete two different calculations for each group of fish. One has been done for you.

...... x 7 = ...

...... x 3 = ...

4 x 3 = 12

3 x 4 = 12

*

3 x ...... = ...

9 x ...... = ...

3 times table

Trace over the dotted numbers and fill in the empty boxes to finish these calculations in the 3 times table.

3 x 1 = ☐   3 x 6 = ☐

3 x 2 = ☐   3 x 7 = ☐

3 x 3 = ☐   3 x 8 = ☐

3 x 4 = ☐   3 x 9 = ☐

3 x 5 = ☐   3 x 10 = ☐

Calculation match-up 23

Help Froggy finish these calculations. Draw a
line to join each one to its answer.
One has been done for you.

How many threes?

24

Finish these calculations. To help, you could draw around groups of 3 bugs, then count the groups.

☐ X 3 = 6
groups
of

☐ X 3 = 18
groups
of

Finish these calculations. To help, you could draw around groups of 3 berries, then count the groups.

$$\boxed{} \times 3 = 21$$

$$\boxed{} \times 3 = 15$$

Missing numbers

Write the missing numbers in the boxes to finish
these calculations from the 3 times table.

◻ x 3 = 6

3 x ◻ = 15

4 x 3 = ◻

3 x ◻ = 27

◻ x 3 = 21

3 x 1 = ◻

How many threes?

Finish these calculations. To help, you could draw
around groups of 3 fireflies, then count the groups.

$\boxed{} \times 3 = 3$

$\boxed{} \times 3 = 9$

How many threes?

Finish these calculations. To help, you could draw around groups of 3 ants, then count the groups.

☐ x 3 = 30

☐ x 3 = 24

Missing numbers

Write the missing numbers in the boxes to finish these calculations from the 3 times table.

$$\boxed{} \times 3 = 9$$

$$3 \times \boxed{} = 24$$

$$6 \times 3 = \boxed{}$$

$$3 \times \boxed{} = 30$$

$$\boxed{} \times 3 = 12$$

$$3 \times 7 = \boxed{}$$

Number wheel

Help Lep complete the number wheel. Multiply each number with 3 to fill in the empty spaces.

Two times three is six.

Groups of 6

This group of 6 monkeys is having fun around the tree. Trace over the numbers in the boxes to finish the sentence.

1 group of 6 monkeys = 6 monkeys altogether.

6   12   18   24   30   36   42   48   54   60

Groups of 6

These groups of 6 bears are paddling their canoes on the river. Count the groups, then write the numbers in the boxes to finish the sentence.

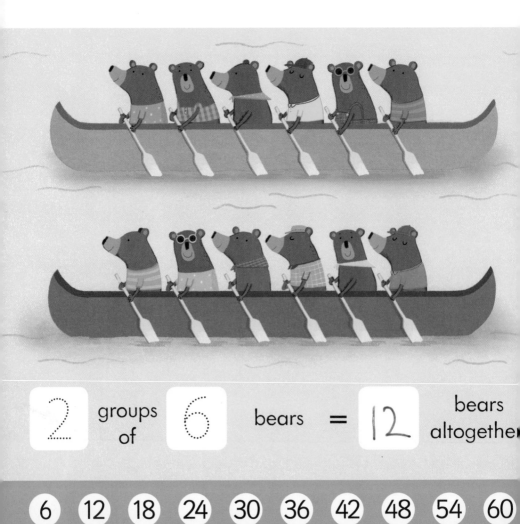

2 groups of 6 bears = 12 bears altogether

6 12 18 24 30 36 42 48 54 60

Adding in sixes

33

Help Tig add up these numbers.
Write the totals in the boxes.

6 12 18 24 30 36 42 48
$6+6+6+6+6+6+6+6+6 = 54$

$6+6+6 = 18$

Hold steady, Crock!

$6+6+6+6 = 24$

$6+6+6+6+6 = 30$

6 12 18 24 30 36 42 48 54 60

Groups of 6

These lily pads grow in groups of 6 on the river.
Count the groups, then write the numbers
in the boxes to finish the sentence.

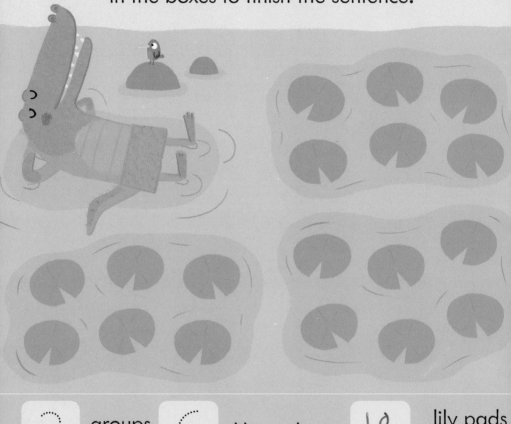

3 groups of 6 lily pads = 18 lily pads altogether

6 12 18 24 30 36 42 48 54 60

Groups of 6

These lily pads grow in groups of 6.
Count the groups, then write the numbers
in the boxes to finish the sentence.

4 groups of 6 lily pads = 24 lily pads altogether.

6 12 18 24 30 36 42 48 54 60

Flower sixes

Help Cheeky count the flowers in sixes. Follow the
arrows, and write the new total under each group.

6 → 12 → 18 → 24

30 ← 36 ← 42 ← 48

54 → 60

I know that all
of the numbers
will be even.

Honeycomb

Find a route across the honeycomb. The next cell's number must always be 6 more than the number of the cell you are on.

Start

12   16

15   11   6   18   22

21   16   18   24   26   28   34

24   26   30   32   34   38

30   34   36   38   40   44   42

36   40   42   48   49   51

40   42   46   50   54   57   55

48   56   58   60   62

54   60

Finish

Groups of 6

These parrots are perching in groups of 6.
Count the groups, then write the numbers
in the boxes to finish the sentence.

5 groups of 6 parrots = 30 parrots altogether

6   12   18   24   30   36   42   48   54   60

Groups of 6

These parrots are perching in groups of 6.
Count the groups, then write the numbers
in the boxes to finish the sentence.

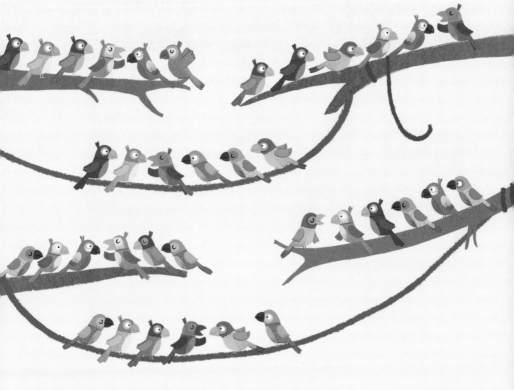

6 groups of 6 parrots = 36 parrots altogether.

6 12 18 24 30 36 42 48 54 60

Sequences

Fill in the missing numbers in these sequences so that each number is 6 more than the one before.

6　12　18　24

36　42　48　54

12　18　24　30

24　30　36　42

Groups of 6

These leopard cubs all have 6 spots on their fur.
Count the cubs, then write the numbers in
the boxes to finish the sentence.

7 cubs with 6 spots = 42 spots altogether.

6   12   18   24   30   36   42   48   54   60

Groups of 6

These leopard cubs all have 6 spots.
Count the cubs, then write the numbers
in the boxes to finish the sentence.

[ ] cubs with [6] spots = [ ] spots altogether

6   12   18   24   30   36   42   48   54   60

Sequences

Fill in the missing numbers in these sequences so that each number is 6 more than the one before.

18 | | | 36

30 | | |

| | 18 |

42 | | |

Groups of 6

These tiger cubs all have 6 stripes on their fur.
Count the cubs, then write the numbers in
the boxes to finish the sentence.

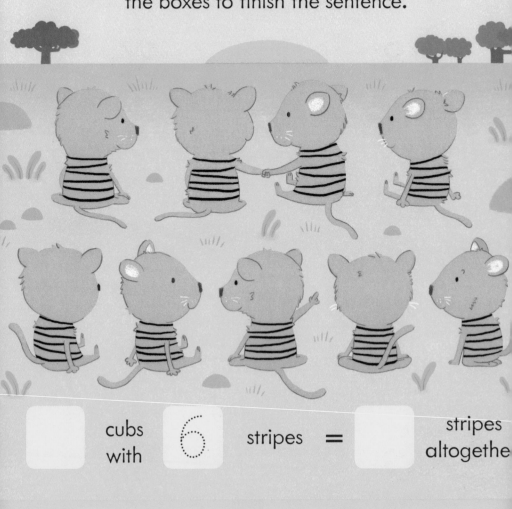

cubs
with

6

stripes = stripes
altogethe

6   12   18   24   30   36   42   48   54   60

Groups of 6

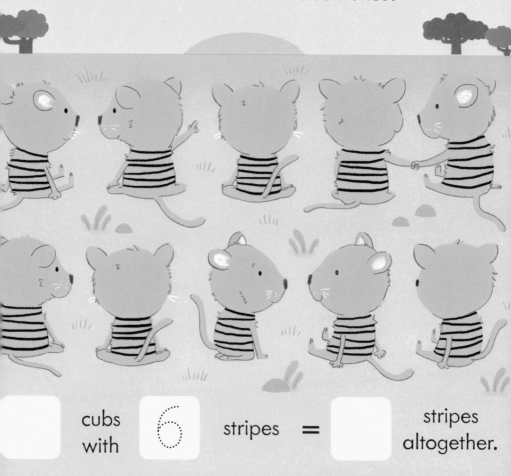

These tiger cubs all have 6 stripes.
Count the cubs, then write the numbers
in the boxes to finish the sentence.

[ ] cubs with [6] stripes = [ ] stripes altogether.

6 12 18 24 30 36 42 48 54 60

6 times table

Trace over the dotted numbers and fill in the empty boxes to finish these calculations in the 6 times table.

1 x 6 = ☐   6 x 6 = ☐

2 x 6 = ☐   7 x 6 = ☐

3 x 6 = ☐   8 x 6 = ☐

4 x 6 = ☐   9 x 6 = ☐

5 x 6 = ☐   10 x 6 = ☐

Calculation pairs

Lep and Baz have been buying party hats. Fill in the numbers in the calculations below to see how many party hats they each have, and to see if Baz is right.

Looks like we both have the same number of party hats, Lep!

Lep's calculation:

$$6 \quad \text{x} \atop \text{rows of} \quad 5 \quad = \quad \boxed{}$$

Baz's calculation:

$$5 \quad \text{x} \atop \text{rows of} \quad 6 \quad = \quad \boxed{}$$

6 groups

These fireflies are in 6 groups. Count how
many fireflies are in each group, then
write the numbers in the boxes.

6   X   [ ]   =   [ ]

(6) (12) (18) (24) (30) (36) (42) (48) (54) (60)

6 groups

These dragonflies are in 6 groups. Count how many dragonflies are in each group, then write the numbers in the boxes.

6 X ☐ = ☐

6   12   18   24   30   36   42   48   54   60

Calculation pairs

Fill in the spaces to complete two different calculations for each group of flowers. One has been done for you.

$$3 \times 6 = 18$$
$$6 \times 3 = 18$$

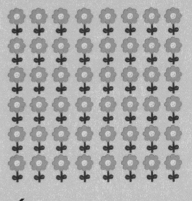

$$6 \times \ldots\ldots = \ldots\ldots$$
$$8 \times \ldots\ldots = \ldots\ldots$$

$$\ldots\ldots \times \ 6 = \ldots\ldots$$
$$\ldots\ldots \times 10 = \ldots\ldots$$

$$\ldots\ldots \times \ldots\ldots = \ldots\ldots$$
$$\ldots\ldots \times \ldots\ldots = \ldots\ldots$$

Calculation pairs

51

Fill in the spaces to complete two different calculations for each group of flowers. One has been done for you.

...... x ...... = ...

...... x ...... = ...

5 x 6 = 30

6 x 5 = 30

...... x 4 = ...

...... x 6 = ...

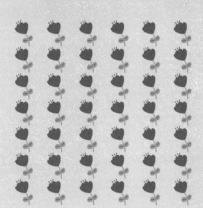

7 x ...... = ...

6 x ...... = ...

6 times table

Trace over the dotted numbers and fill in the empty boxes to finish these calculations in the 6 times table.

6 x 1 = ☐   6 x 6 = ☐

6 x 2 = ☐   6 x 7 = ☐

6 x 3 = ☐   6 x 8 = ☐

6 x 4 = ☐   6 x 9 = ☐

6 x 5 = ☐   6 x 10 = ☐

Calculation match-up 53

Help Lep finish these calculations. Draw a
line to join each one to its answer.
One has been done for you.

6 x 9

18   60   2 x 6

5 x 6

6 x 3   54

42   10 x 6

8 x 6   30

12   48

6 x 7

How many sixes?

Finish these calculations. To help, you could draw around groups of 6 bugs, then count the groups.

[ ] X 6 = 30
groups
of

[ ] X 6 = 42
groups
of

Finish these calculations. To help, you could draw around groups of 6 berries, then count the groups.

☐ x 6 = 24

☐ x 6 = 48

Missing numbers

Write the missing numbers in the boxes to finish
these calculations from the 6 times table.

$\boxed{} \times 6 = 42$

$6 \times \boxed{} = 12$

$4 \times 6 = \boxed{}$

$6 \times \boxed{} = 48$

$\boxed{} \times 6 = 60$

$6 \times 1 = \boxed{}$

How many sixes?

Finish these calculations. To help, you could draw around groups of 6 fireflies, then count the groups.

☐ x 6 = 6

☐ x 6 = 36

How many sixes?

Finish these calculations. To help, you could draw
around groups of 6 ants, then count the groups.

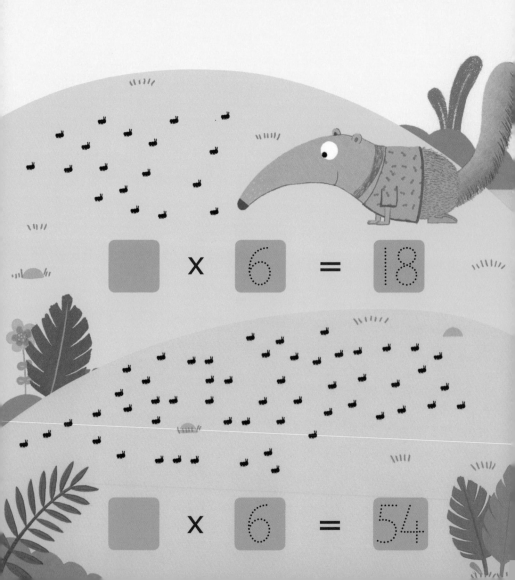

☐ x 6 = 18

☐ x 6 = 54

Missing numbers

Write the missing numbers in the boxes to finish
these calculations from the 6 times table.

$\boxed{}$ x 6 = 24

6 x $\boxed{}$ = 36

8 x 6 = $\boxed{}$

6 x $\boxed{}$ = 18

$\boxed{}$ x 6 = 54

6 x 5 = $\boxed{}$

Number wheel

Help Lep complete the number wheel. Multiply each number with 6 to fill in the empty spaces.

x6

1 5
7 3
4 x6 9
6 10
8 2
12

x6

Two times six
is twelve.

Calculation pairs

Help the animals complete these calculations for
numbers that are in both the 3 and 6 times tables.

6 x 3 = 18
3 x 6 = 18

...... x 3 = 24
...... x 6 = 24

3 x ...... = 12
6 x .... = 12

3 x ...... = 30
6 x ...... = 30

...... x 3 = 6
...... x 6 = 6

Calculation match-up

Help Froggy finish drawing lines to join each
answer to **two** calculations that equal it.

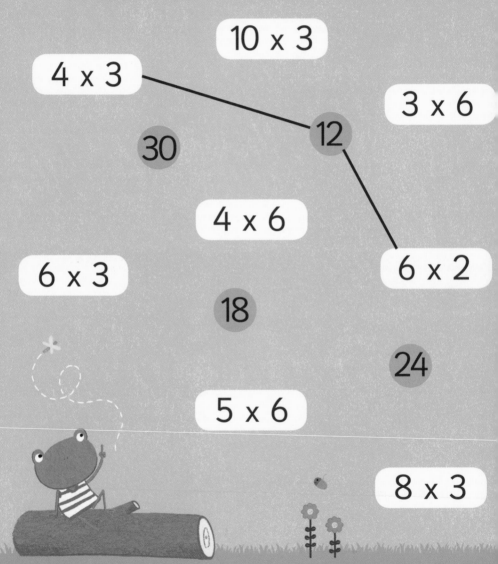

10 x 3

4 x 3

3 x 6

12

30

4 x 6

6 x 3

6 x 2

18

24

5 x 6

8 x 3

Patterns of 3 and 6

Help the mice draw around the numbers from the 3 and 6 times tables.

1	2	③	4	5	⑥
7	8	9	10	11	12
13	14	15	16	17	18
19	20	21	22	23	24
25	26	27	28	29	30
31	32	33	34	35	36
37	38	39	40	41	42
43	44	45	46	47	48
49	50	51	52	53	54
55	56	57	58	59	60

Help me circle the numbers in the 3 times table.

Can you draw a triangle around each number in the 6 times table for me?

Write the missing numbers in the boxes to finish these calculations from the 3 and 6 times tables.

$\boxed{} \times 6 = 24$

$3 \times \boxed{} = 15$

$9 \times 3 = \boxed{}$

$6 \times \boxed{} = 36$

$\boxed{} \times 3 = 21$

$3 \times 6 = \boxed{}$

Write the missing numbers in the boxes to finish these calculations from the 3 and 6 times tables.

$\boxed{}$ x 3 = 9

6 x $\boxed{}$ = 54

8 x 3 = $\boxed{}$

6 x $\boxed{}$ = 42

$\boxed{}$ x 6 = 30

3 x 4 = $\boxed{}$

This group of 4 monkeys is having fun around the tree. Trace over the numbers in the boxes to finish the sentence.

1 group of 4 monkeys = 4 monkeys altogether

4 8 12 16 20 24 28 32 36 40

Groups of 4

These groups of 4 bears are paddling their canoes on the river. Count the groups, then write the numbers in the boxes to finish the sentence.

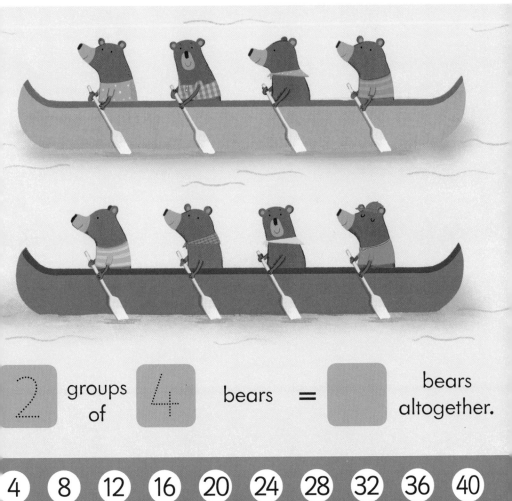

2 groups of 4 bears = ☐ bears altogether.

4   8   12   16   20   24   28   32   36   40

Adding in fours

Help Lem add up these numbers.
Write the totals in the boxes.

$$4 + 4 + 4 + 4 + 4 + 4 + 4 = \boxed{}$$

$$4 + 4 + 4 + 4 + 4 + 4 = \boxed{}$$

Hold steady,
Baz!

$$4 + 4 = \boxed{}$$

$$4 + 4 + 4 = \boxed{}$$

4   8   12   16   20   24   28   32   36   40

Groups of 4

These lily pads grow in groups of 4 on the river.
Count the groups, then write the numbers
in the boxes to finish the sentence.

3 groups of 4 lily pads = ☐ lily pads altogether.

4   8   12   16   20   24   28   32   36   40

Groups of 4

These lily pads grow in groups of 4.
Count the groups, then write the numbers
in the boxes to finish the sentence.

4 groups of 4 lily pads = ☐ lily pads altogethe

4　8　12　16　20　24　28　32　36　40

Flower fours

Help Tan-tan count the flowers in fours. Follow the arrows, and write the new total under each group.

I know that all of the numbers will be even.

Honeycomb

72

Find a route across the honeycomb. The next cell's number must always be 4 more than the number of the cell you are on.

Start

14 18

4 8 11 16 20

6 10 12 14 19 22 26

14 18 16 20 23 25

21 20 22 26 24 30 29

25 28 30 28 32 34

31 29 32 34 36 35 37

35 36 40 38 41

39 42

Finish

Groups of 4

These parrots are perching in groups of 4.
Count the groups, then write the numbers
in the boxes to finish the sentence.

| | groups of | 4 | parrots | = | | parrots altogether. |

4   8   12   16   20   24   28   32   36   40

Groups of 4

These parrots are perching in groups of 4.
Count the groups, then write the numbers
in the boxes to finish the sentence.

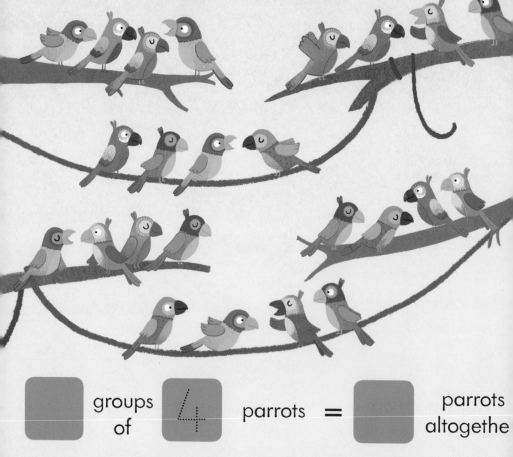

☐ groups of 4 parrots = ☐ parrots altogethe

4 8 12 16 20 24 28 32 36 40

Sequences

Fill in the missing numbers in these sequences so that each number is 4 more than the one before.

4 ☐ 12 ☐

24 ☐ ☐ 36

8 ☐ ☐ 20

16 ☐ ☐ ☐

Groups of 4

These leopard cubs all have 4 spots on their fur.
Count the cubs, then write the numbers in
the boxes to finish the sentence.

| | cubs with | 4 | spots | = | | spots altogether |

4   8   12   16   20   24   28   32   36   40

Groups of 4

These leopard cubs all have 4 spots.
Count the cubs, then write the numbers
in the boxes to finish the sentence.

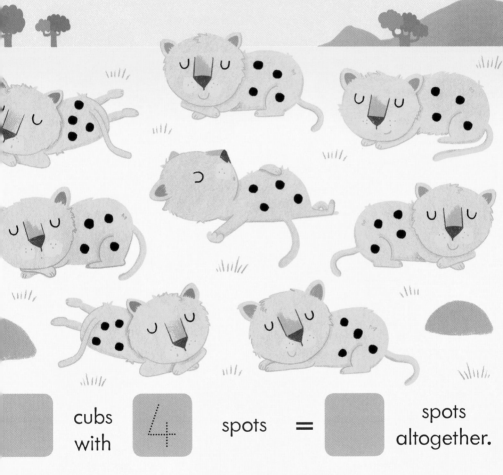

cubs
with

4

spots

=

spots
altogether.

4 8 12 16 20 24 28 32 36 40

Sequences

Fill in the missing numbers in these sequences so that each number is 4 more than the one before.

| 12 | | | 24 |

| 20 | | | |

| | | 12 | |

| 28 | | | |

Groups of 4

These tiger cubs all have 4 stripes on their fur.
Count the cubs, then write the numbers in
the boxes to finish the sentence.

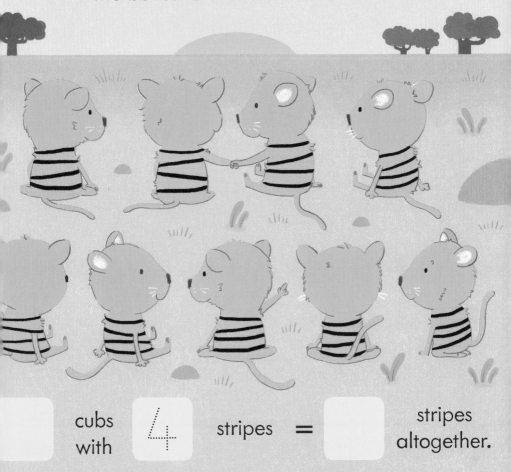

cubs
with   4   stripes   =   stripes
                                      altogether.

4   8   12   16   20   24   28   32   36   40

Groups of 4

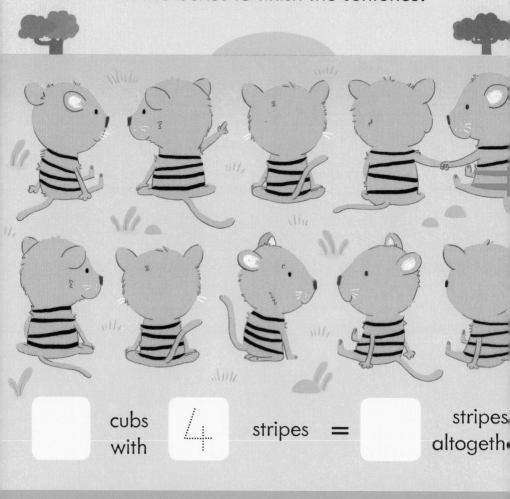

These tiger cubs all have 4 stripes.
Count the cubs, then write the numbers
in the boxes to finish the sentence.

[ ] cubs with 4 stripes = [ ] stripes altogeth

4   8   12   16   20   24   28   32   36   4C

4 times table

81

Trace over the dotted numbers and fill in the empty boxes to finish these calculations in the 4 times table.

1 x 4 = ☐   6 x 4 = ☐

2 x 4 = ☐   7 x 4 = ☐

3 x 4 = ☐   8 x 4 = ☐

4 x 4 = ☐   9 x 4 = ☐

5 x 4 = ☐   10 x 4 = ☐

Calculation pairs

Baz and Lep have been growing flowers. Fill in the numbers in the calculations below to see how many flowers they each have, and to see if Baz is right.

I think we both have the same number of flowers, Lep!

Baz's calculation:

4 x rows of 7 =

Lep's calculation:

7 x rows of 4 =

4 groups

These flowers are in 4 groups. Count how many flowers are in each group, then write the numbers in the boxes.

4 X ☐ = ☐

4   8   12   16   20   24   28   32   36   40

4 groups

These birds are in 4 groups. Count how
many birds are in each group, then
write the numbers in the boxes.

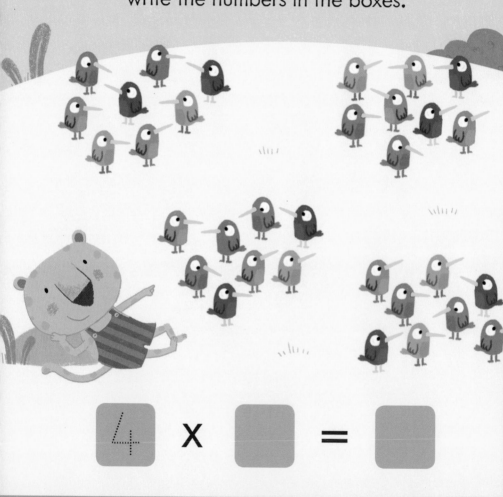

| 4 | X | | = | |

4 8 12 16 20 24 28 32 36 40

Calculation pairs

85

ill in the spaces to complete two different calculations
for each group of fruit. One has been done for you.

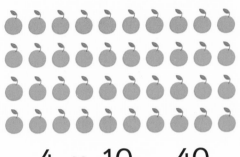

4 x 10 = 40
10 x 4 = 40

...... x 4 = ...
...... x 3 = ...

9 x ...... = ...
4 x ...... = ...

7 x ...... = ...
4 x ...... = ...

Calculation pairs

Fill in the spaces to complete two different calculation
for each group of bugs. One has been done for you.

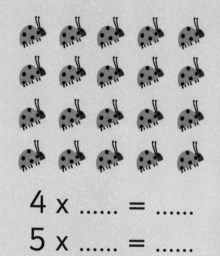

$4 \times 6 = 24$

$6 \times 4 = 24$

$4 \times$ ...... = ...

$5 \times$ ...... = ...

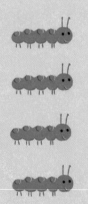

$4 \times$ ...... = ...

...... $\times 4 =$ ......

$4 \times$ ...... = ...

$8 \times$ ...... = ...

4 times table

Trace over the dotted numbers and fill in the empty boxes to finish these calculations in the 4 times table.

4 x 1 = ☐   4 x 6 = ☐

4 x 2 = ☐   4 x 7 = ☐

4 x 3 = ☐   4 x 8 = ☐

4 x 4 = ☐   4 x 9 = ☐

4 x 5 = ☐   4 x 10 = ☐

Calculation match-up

Help Baz finish these calculations. Draw a
line to join each one to its answer.
One has been done for you.

4 x 2

12

4 x 7

24

20

32

5 x 4

4 x 9

8

28

4 x 6

8 x 4

36

3 x 4

How many fours?

Finish these calculations. To help, you could draw around groups of 4 bugs, then count the groups.

$$\boxed{} \times \boxed{4} = \boxed{4}$$

group of

$$\boxed{} \times \boxed{4} = \boxed{16}$$

groups of

How many fours?

90

Finish these calculations. To help, you could draw
around groups of 4 berries, then count the groups.

☐ x 4 = 24

☐ x 4 = 12

Missing numbers

Write the missing numbers in the boxes to finish these calculations from the 4 times table.

$\boxed{} \times 4 = 4$

$4 \times \boxed{} = 28$

$4 \times 4 = \boxed{}$

$4 \times \boxed{} = 36$

$\boxed{} \times 4 = 20$

$2 \times 4 = \boxed{}$

How many fours?

Finish these calculations. To help, you could draw around groups of 4 fireflies, then count the groups.

$\boxed{} \times 4 = 28$

$\boxed{} \times 4 = 36$

How many fours?

Finish these calculations. To help, you could draw around groups of 4 ants, then count the groups.

☐ x 4 = 32

☐ x 4 = 8

Missing numbers

Write the missing numbers in the boxes to finish
these calculations from the 4 times table.

☐ x 4 = 12

4 x ☐ = 20

7 x 4 = ☐

4 x ☐ = 40

☐ x 4 = 24

8 x 4 = ☐

Number wheel

Help Lep complete the number wheel. Multiply each number with 4 to fill in the empty spaces.

x4

Three times four is twelve.

Groups of 8

This group of 8 monkeys is having fun around the tree. Trace over the numbers in the boxes to finish the sentence.

1 group of 8 monkeys = 8 monkeys altogether

8 16 24 32 40 48 56 64 72 80

Groups of 8

These groups of 8 bears are paddling their canoes on the river. Count the groups, then write the numbers in the boxes to finish the sentence.

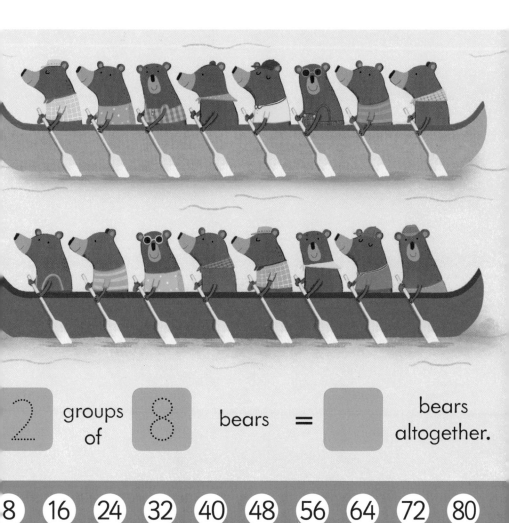

2 groups of 8 bears = ☐ bears altogether.

8 16 24 32 40 48 56 64 72 80

Adding in eights

Help Lem add up these numbers.
Write the totals in the boxes.

$$8 + 8 + 8 + 8 + 8 + 8 + 8 = \boxed{}$$

Hold steady, Baz!

$$8 + 8 + 8 + 8 = \boxed{}$$

$$8 + 8 + 8 + 8 + 8 = \boxed{}$$

$$8 + 8 + 8 + 8 + 8 + 8 = \boxed{}$$

8 16 24 32 40 48 56 64 72 80

Groups of 8

These lily pads grow in groups of 8 on the river.
Count the groups, then write the numbers
in the boxes to finish the sentence.

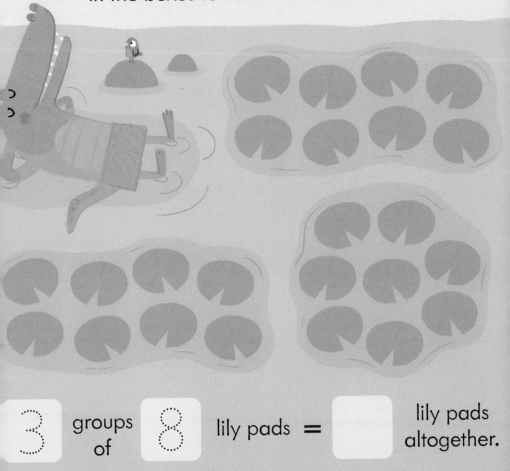

3 groups of 8 lily pads = ☐ lily pads altogether.

8 16 24 32 40 48 56 64 72 80

Groups of 8

100

These lily pads grow in groups of 8.
Count the groups, then write the numbers
in the boxes to finish the sentence.

4 groups of 8 lily pads = ☐ lily pads altogether

8 16 24 32 40 48 56 64 72 80

Flower eights

Help Tig count the flowers in eights. Follow the arrows, and write the new total under each group.

8 → 16 →

I know that all of the numbers will be even.

Honeycomb

Find a route across the honeycomb. The next cell's number must always be 8 more than the number of the cell you are on.

Start

26 34

8   14 20 30 38

16 18 22 28 44 46 52

24 26 24 32 48 58

30 32 28 36 54 56 64

38 40 48 56 62 72

44 46 52 66 64 70 76

60 74 72 78 84

68 80

Finish

Groups of 8

These parrots are perching in groups of 8.
Count the groups, then write the numbers
in the boxes to finish the sentence.

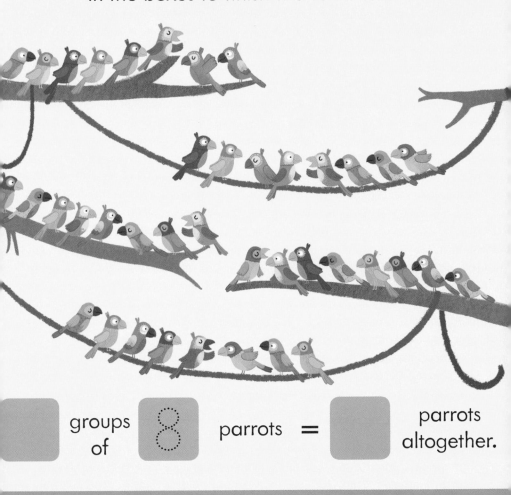

[ ] groups of 8 parrots = [ ] parrots altogether.

8   16   24   32   40   48   56   64   72   80

Groups of 8

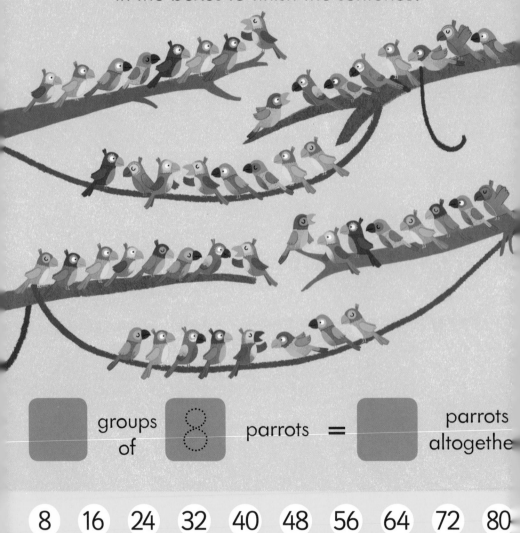

These parrots are perching in groups of 8.
Count the groups, then write the numbers
in the boxes to finish the sentence.

☐ groups of 8 parrots = ☐ parrots altogethe

8   16   24   32   40   48   56   64   72   80

Sequences

Fill in the missing numbers in these sequences so that each number is 8 more than the one before.

8		24	
48			72
16			40
32			

Groups of 8

These leopard cubs all have 8 spots on their fur.
Count the cubs, then write the numbers in
the boxes to finish the sentence.

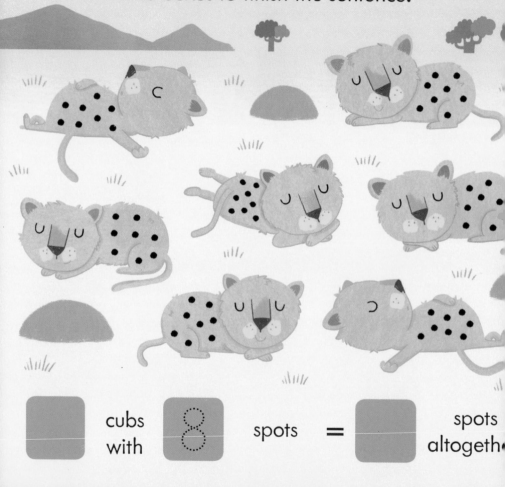

| | cubs with | 8 | spots | = | | spots altogeth |

8   16   24   32   40   48   56   64   72   80

Groups of 8

These leopard cubs all have 8 spots.
Count the cubs, then write the numbers
in the boxes to finish the sentence.

| | cubs with | 8 | spots | = | | spots altogether. |

8 16 24 32 40 48 56 64 72 80

Sequences

Fill in the missing numbers in these sequences so that each number is 8 more than the one before.

| 24 | | | 48 |

| 40 | | | |

| | | 24 | |

| 56 | | | |

These tiger cubs all have 8 stripes on their fur.
Count the cubs, then write the numbers in
the boxes to finish the sentence.

[ ] cubs with 8 stripes = [ ] stripes altogether.

8 16 24 32 40 48 56 64 72 80

Groups of 8

These tiger cubs all have 8 stripes.
Count the cubs, then write the numbers
in the boxes to finish the sentence.

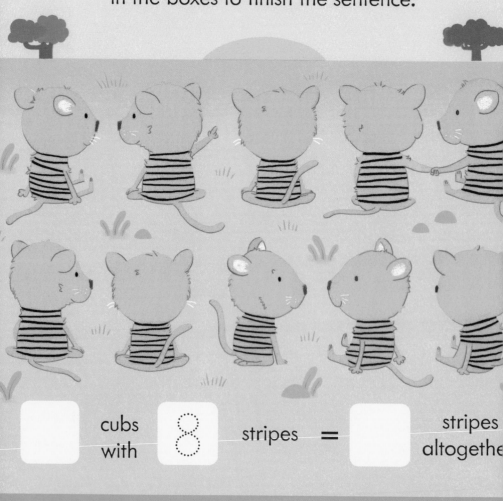

☐ cubs with 8 stripes = ☐ stripes altogether

8 16 24 32 40 48 56 64 72 80

8 times table

Trace over the dotted numbers and fill in the empty boxes to finish these calculations in the 8 times table.

1 x 8 = ☐   6 x 8 = ☐

2 x 8 = ☐   7 x 8 = ☐

3 x 8 = ☐   8 x 8 = ☐

4 x 8 = ☐   9 x 8 = ☐

5 x 8 = ☐   10 x 8 = ☐

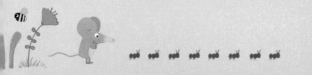

Calculation pairs

112

Lep and Baz have been picking mangoes. Fill in the numbers in the calculations below to see how many mangoes they each have, and to see if Baz is right.

Looks like we both have the same number of mangoes, Lep!

Lep's calculation:

8 x rows of **2** =

Baz's calculation:

2 x rows of **8** =

8 groups

These ants are in 8 groups. Count how many ants are in each group, then write the numbers in the boxes.

$$8 \times \boxed{} = \boxed{}$$

8 16 24 32 40 48 56 64 72 80

8 groups

These butterflies are in 8 groups. Count how many butterflies are in each group, then write the numbers in the boxes.

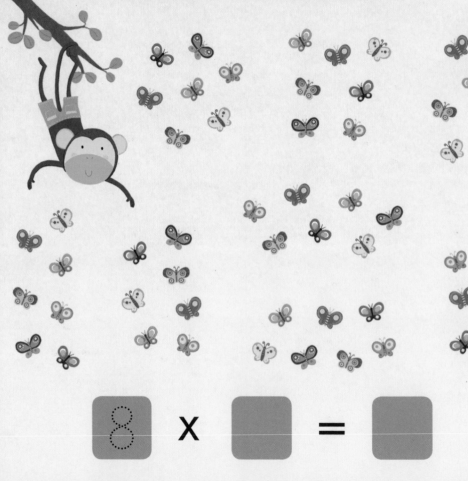

$$8 \times \boxed{} = \boxed{}$$

8 16 24 32 40 48 56 64 72 80

Calculation pairs

Fill in the spaces to complete two different calculations for each group of objects. One has been done for you.

$3 \text{ x } \text{.....} = \text{.....}$

$8 \text{ x } \text{.....} = \text{.....}$

$8 \text{ x } 6 = 48$

$6 \text{ x } 8 = 48$

$\text{.....} \text{ x } 8 = \text{.....}$

$\text{.....} \text{ x } 1 = \text{.....}$

$\text{.....} \text{ x } \text{.....} = \text{.....}$

$\text{.....} \text{ x } \text{.....} = \text{.....}$

Calculation pairs

Fill in the spaces to complete two different calculation
for each group of objects. One has been done for you

2 x ...... = ...

8 x ...... = ...

4 x 8 = 32

8 x 4 = 32

...... x 5 = ...

...... x 8 = ...

8 x ...... = ...

9 x ...... = ...

8 times table

Trace over the dotted numbers and fill in the empty boxes to finish these calculations in the 8 times table.

8 x 1 = ☐   8 x 6 = ☐

8 x 2 = ☐   8 x 7 = ☐

8 x 3 = ☐   8 x 8 = ☐

8 x 4 = ☐   8 x 9 = ☐

8 x 5 = ☐   8 x 10 = ☐

Calculation match-up

Help Ant finish these calculations. Draw a
line to join each one to its answer.
One has been done for you.

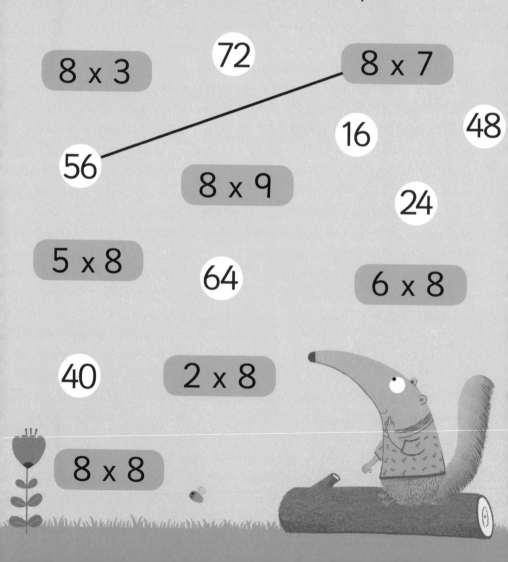

72

8 x 3   8 x 7

16   48

56

8 x 9

24

5 x 8

64   6 x 8

40   2 x 8

8 x 8

How many eights?

Finish these calculations. To help, you could draw around groups of 8 bugs, then count the groups.

☐ X 8 = 24
groups of

☐ X 8 = 40
groups of

How many eights?

Finish these calculations. To help, you could draw around groups of 8 berries, then count the groups.

$$\boxed{} \times 8 = 56$$

$$\boxed{} \times 8 = 80$$

Missing numbers

Write the missing numbers in the boxes to finish these calculations from the 8 times table.

☐ x 8 = 24

8 x ☐ = 48

2 x 8 = ☐

8 x ☐ = 32

☐ x 8 = 56

8 x 10 = ☐

How many eights?

Finish these calculations. To help, you could draw around groups of 8 fireflies, then count the groups.

☐ x 8 = 16

☐ x 8 = 64

How many eights?

Finish these calculations. To help, you could draw around groups of 8 ants, then count the groups.

☐ x 8 = 32

☐ x 8 = 72

Missing numbers

Write the missing numbers in the boxes to finish these calculations from the 8 times table.

☐ x 8 = 8

8 x ☐ = 72

6 x 8 = ☐

8 x ☐ = 24

☐ x 8 = 40

8 x 8 = ☐

Number wheel

Help Lep complete the number wheel. Multiply each number with 8 to fill in the empty spaces.

x8

One times eight is eight.

Calculation pairs

Help the animals complete these calculations for numbers that are in both the 4 and 8 times tables.

4 x 4 = 16
2 x 8 = 16

4 x ...... = 24
8 x ...... = 24

...... x 4 = 40
...... x 8 = 40

4 x ...... = 32
8 x ...... = 32

...... x 4 = 8
...... x 8 = 8

Calculation match-up

Help Lep finish drawing lines to join each
answer to **two** calculations that equal it.

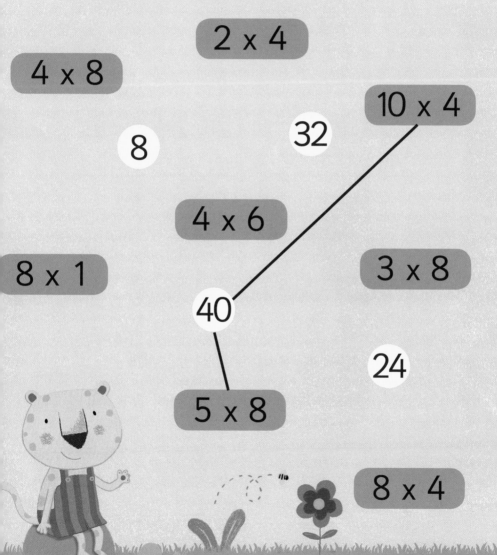

2 x 4

4 x 8

10 x 4

8

32

4 x 6

8 x 1

3 x 8

40

24

5 x 8

8 x 4

Patterns of 4 and 8

Help the mice draw around the numbers
from the 4 and 8 times tables.

1	2	3	④	5	6	7	⑧
9	10	11	12	13	14	15	16
17	18	19	20	21	22	23	24
25	26	27	28	29	30	31	32
33	34	35	36	37	38	39	40
41	42	43	44	45	46	47	48
49	50	51	52	53	54	55	56
57	58	59	60	61	62	63	64
65	66	67	68	69	70	71	72
73	74	75	76	77	78	79	80

Help me circle the numbers
in the 4 times table.

Can you draw a triangle
around each number in the
8 times table for me?

Missing numbers

Write the missing numbers in the boxes to finish these calculations from the 4 and 8 times tables.

$\boxed{} \times 4 = 36$

$8 \times \boxed{} = 16$

$4 \times 7 = \boxed{}$

$8 \times \boxed{} = 80$

$\boxed{} \times 8 = 48$

$4 \times 4 = \boxed{}$

Missing numbers

Write the missing numbers in the boxes to finish these calculations from the 4 and 8 times tables.

$\boxed{} \times 8 = 32$

$8 \times \boxed{} = 72$

$4 \times 5 = \boxed{}$

$8 \times \boxed{} = 24$

$\boxed{} \times 4 = 12$

$7 \times 8 = \boxed{}$

Correct calculations

Help Tan-tan draw around the calculations in
each row that equal the answer at the end.
There may be more than one in some rows.

8 x 8	10 x 6	9 x 8	6 x 9	72

4 x 4	3 x 5	2 x 8	7 x 6	16

2 x 6	5 x 3	6 x 3	3 x 4	12

6 x 10	7 x 8	9 x 4	8 x 6	56

Correct calculations

Help Tan-tan draw around the calculations in each row that equal the answer at the end. There may be more than one in some rows.

6×3 4×4 2×8 3×5 **15**

9×4 3×10 6×6 5×8 **36**

9×8 4×7 6×10 8×8 **64**

4×6 5×8 6×4 8×3 **24**

Mixed tables

Write the missing numbers in the boxes
to complete these calculations.

☐ x 3 = 15

8 x ☐ = 32

9 x 6 = ☐

7 x ☐ = 56

☐ x 10 = 40

3 x 3 = ☐

Mixed tables

Write the missing numbers in the boxes
to complete these calculations.

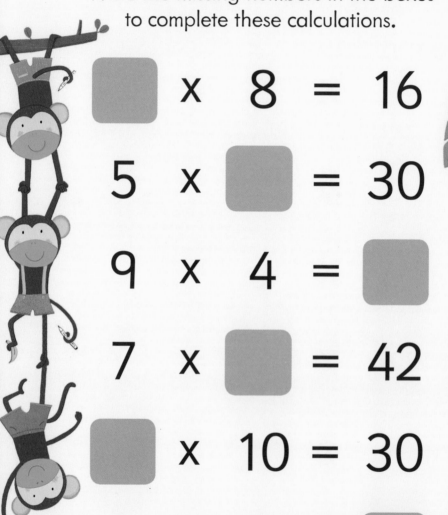

$\boxed{} \times 8 = 16$

$5 \times \boxed{} = 30$

$9 \times 4 = \boxed{}$

$7 \times \boxed{} = 42$

$\boxed{} \times 10 = 30$

$8 \times 5 = \boxed{}$

Mixed tables

Write the missing numbers in the boxes
to complete these calculations.

$\boxed{} \times 7 = 21$

$4 \times \boxed{} = 36$

$6 \times 6 = \boxed{}$

$3 \times \boxed{} = 12$

$\boxed{} \times 10 = 60$

$9 \times 8 = \boxed{}$

Mixed tables

Write the missing numbers in the boxes
to complete these calculations.

$\boxed{} \times 6 = 24$

$3 \times \boxed{} = 27$

$8 \times 6 = \boxed{}$

$4 \times \boxed{} = 16$

$\boxed{} \times 8 = 64$

$6 \times 3 = \boxed{}$

Mixed tables

Write the missing numbers in the boxes
to complete these calculations.

$\boxed{} \times 3 = 6$

$8 \times \boxed{} = 80$

$5 \times 4 = \boxed{}$

$2 \times \boxed{} = 8$

$\boxed{} \times 3 = 24$

$6 \times 4 = \boxed{}$

Mixed tables

Write the missing numbers in the boxes
to complete these calculations.

$\boxed{} \times 4 = 28$

$6 \times \boxed{} = 48$

$3 \times 6 = \boxed{}$

$4 \times \boxed{} = 12$

$\boxed{} \times 6 = 60$

$8 \times 7 = \boxed{}$

The 3 times table

Cheeky has written out the 3 times table below to help you to learn and remember it.

1 x 3 = 3

7 x 3 = 21

2 x 3 = 6

8 x 3 = 24

3 x 3 = 9

9 x 3 = 27

4 x 3 = 12

10 x 3 = 30

5 x 3 = 15

6 x 3 = 18

The 6 times table

Cheeky has written out the 6 times table below to help you to learn and remember it.

1 x 6 = 6

7 x 6 = 42

2 x 6 = 12

8 x 6 = 48

3 x 6 = 18

9 x 6 = 54

4 x 6 = 24

10 x 6 = 60

5 x 6 = 30

6 x 6 = 36

The 4 times table

Cheeky has written out the 4 times table
below to help you to learn and remember it.

1 x 4 = 4

7 x 4 = 28

2 x 4 = 8

8 x 4 = 32

3 x 4 = 12

9 x 4 = 36

4 x 4 = 16

10 x 4 = 40

5 x 4 = 20

6 x 4 = 24

The 8 times table

Cheeky has written out the 8 times table
below to help you to learn and remember it.

1 x 8 = 8

7 x 8 = 56

2 x 8 = 16

8 x 8 = 64

3 x 8 = 24

9 x 8 = 72

4 x 8 = 32

10 x 8 = 80

5 x 8 = 40

6 x 8 = 48

Answers

Groups of 3   1

This group of 3 monkeys is having fun around the tree. Trace over the numbers in the boxes to finish the sentence.

1 group of   3 monkeys = 3 monkeys altogether.

3 6 9 12 15 18 21 24 27 30

Groups of 3   2

These groups of 3 bears are paddling their canoes on the river. Count the groups, then write the numbers in the boxes to finish the sentence.

2 groups of   3 bears = 6 bears altogether.

3 6 9 12 15 18 21 24 27 30

Adding in threes   3

Help Tig add up these numbers. Write the totals in the boxes.

3 + 3 + 3 + 3 + 3 + 3 + 3 + 3 = 24

3 + 3 + 3 + 3 + 3 = 15

Hold steady, Crock!

3 + 3 + 3 = 9

3 + 3 + 3 + 3 = 12

3 6 9 12 15 18 21 24 27 30

Groups of 3   4

These lily pads grow in groups of 3 on the river. Count the groups, then write the numbers in the boxes to finish the sentence.

3 groups of   3 lily pads = 9 lily pads altogether.

3 6 9 12 15 18 21 24 27 30

Groups of 3   5

These lily pads grow in groups of 3. Count the groups, then write the numbers in the boxes to finish the sentence.

4 groups of   3 lily pads = 12 lily pads altogether.

3 6 9 12 15 18 21 24 27 30

Flower threes   6

Help Lem count the flowers in threes. Follow the arrows, and write the new total under each group.

3 → 6 → 9 → 12

24 ← 21 ← 18 ← 15

I know the numbers will alternate between odd and even.

27 → 30

Honeycomb   7

Find a route across the honeycomb. The next cell's number must always be 3 more than the number of the cell you are on.

Start

14 17
5 9 11 16 20
8 10 13 19 23 25
12 16 17 21 26
10 16 18 22 24 27
18 23 22 21 24 28
20 21 24 25 26 31
26 27 28 29 30
29 32
Finish

Groups of 3   8

These parrots are perching in groups of 3. Count the groups, then write the numbers in the boxes to finish the sentence.

5 groups of   3 parrots = 15 parrots altogether.

3 6 9 12 15 18 21 24 27 30

Groups of 3   9

These parrots are perching in groups of 3. Count the groups, then write the numbers in the boxes to finish the sentence.

6 groups of   3 parrots = 18 parrots altogether.

3 6 9 12 15 18 21 24 27 30

Answers

Sequences 10

Fill in the missing numbers in these sequences so that each number is 3 more than the one before.

3 6 9 12

18 21 24 27

6 9 12 15

12 15 18 21

Groups of 3 11

These leopard cubs all have 3 spots on their fur. Count the cubs, then write the numbers in the boxes to finish the sentence.

7 cubs with 3 spots = 21 spots altogether

3 6 9 12 15 18 21 24 27 30

Groups of 3 12

These leopard cubs all have 3 spots. Count the cubs, then write the numbers in the boxes to finish the sentence.

8 cubs with 3 spots = 24 spots altogether

3 6 9 12 15 18 21 24 27 30

Sequences 13

Fill in the missing numbers in these sequences so that each number is 3 more than the one before.

9 12 15 18

15 18 21 24

3 6 9 12

21 24 27 30

Groups of 3 14

These tiger cubs all have 3 stripes on their fur. Count the cubs, then write the numbers in the boxes to finish the sentence.

9 cubs with 3 stripes = 27 stripes altogether

3 6 9 12 15 18 21 24 27 30

Groups of 3 15

These tiger cubs all have 3 stripes. Count the cubs, then write the numbers in the boxes to finish the sentence.

10 cubs with 3 stripes = 30 stripes altogether

3 6 9 12 15 18 21 24 27 30

3 times table 16

Trace over the dotted numbers and fill in the empty boxes to finish these calculations in the 3 times table.

$1 \times 3 = 3$ $6 \times 3 = 18$

$2 \times 3 = 6$ $7 \times 3 = 21$

$3 \times 3 = 9$ $8 \times 3 = 24$

$4 \times 3 = 12$ $9 \times 3 = 27$

$5 \times 3 = 15$ $10 \times 3 = 30$

Calculation pairs 17

Lep and Baz have been picking oranges. Fill in the numbers in the calculations below to see how many oranges they each have, and to see if Baz is right.

I think we both have the same number of oranges, Lep!

Lep's calculation: 9 × rows of 3 = 27

Baz's calculation: 3 × rows of 9 = 27

3 groups 18

These mice are in 3 groups. Count how many mice are in each group, then write the numbers in the boxes.

$3 \times 4 = 12$

3 6 9 12 15 18 21 24 27 30

Answers

3 groups · 19

These bugs are in 3 groups. Count how many bugs are in each group, then write the numbers in the boxes.

$3 \times 7 = 21$

3 6 9 12 15 18 21 24 27 30

Calculation pairs · 20

Fill in the spaces to complete two different calculations for each group of fish. One has been done for you.

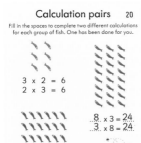

$3 \times 2 = 6$
$2 \times 3 = 6$

$8 \times 3 = 24$
$3 \times 8 = 24$

$3 \times 6 = 18$
$6 \times 3 = 18$

Calculation pairs · 21

Fill in the spaces to complete two different calculations for each group of fish. One has been done for you.

$3 \times 7 = 21$
$7 \times 3 = 21$

$4 \times 3 = 12$
$3 \times 4 = 12$

$3 \times 9 = 27$
$9 \times 3 = 27$

3 times table · 22

Trace over the dotted numbers and fill in the empty boxes to finish these calculations in the 3 times table.

$3 \times 1 = 3$ $3 \times 6 = 18$

$3 \times 2 = 6$ $3 \times 7 = 21$

$3 \times 3 = 9$ $3 \times 8 = 24$

$3 \times 4 = 12$ $3 \times 9 = 27$

$3 \times 5 = 15$ $3 \times 10 = 30$

Calculation match-up · 23

Help Froggy finish these calculations. Draw a line to join each one to its answer. One has been done for you.

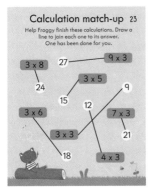

3×8 27 9×3
24 3×5
15 12 9
3×6 7×3
3×3 21
18 4×3

How many threes? · 24

Finish these calculations. To help, you could draw around groups of 3 bugs, then count the groups.

$2 \times 3 = 6$ groups of

$6 \times 3 = 18$ groups of

How many threes? · 25

Finish these calculations. To help, you could draw around groups of 3 berries, then count the groups.

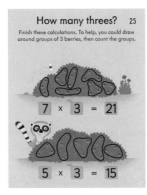

$7 \times 3 = 21$

$5 \times 3 = 15$

Missing numbers · 26

Write the missing numbers in the boxes to finish these calculations from the 3 times table.

$2 \times 3 = 6$

$3 \times 5 = 15$

$4 \times 3 = 12$

$3 \times 9 = 27$

$7 \times 3 = 21$

$3 \times 1 = 3$

How many threes? · 27

Finish these calculations. To help, you could draw around groups of 3 fireflies, then count the groups.

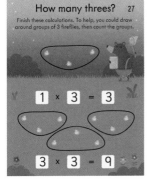

$1 \times 3 = 3$

$3 \times 3 = 9$

Answers

How many threes? 28
Finish these calculations. To help, you could draw around groups of 3 ants, then count the groups.

10 × 3 = 30

8 × 3 = 24

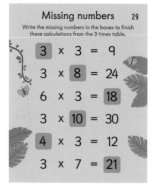

Missing numbers 29
Write the missing numbers in the boxes to finish these calculations from the 3 times table.

3 × 3 = 9

3 × 8 = 24

6 × 3 = 18

3 × 10 = 30

4 × 3 = 12

3 × 7 = 21

Number wheel 30
Help Lep complete the number wheel. Multiply each number with 3 to fill in the empty spaces.

3 15
21 1 5 9
7 3
12 4 ×3 9 27
6 10
18 8 2 30
24 6

×3

Two times three is six.

Groups of 6 31
This group of 6 monkeys is having fun around the tree. Trace over the numbers in the boxes to finish the sentence.

1 group of 6 monkeys = 6 monkeys altogether.

6 12 18 24 30 36 42 48 54 60

Groups of 6 32
These groups of 6 bears are paddling their canoes on the river. Count the groups, then write the numbers in the boxes to finish the sentence.

2 groups of 6 bears = 12 bears altogether.

6 12 18 24 30 36 42 48 54 60

Adding in sixes 33
Help Tig add up these numbers. Write the totals in the boxes.

6 + 6 + 6 + 6 + 6 + 6 + 6 + 6 + 6 = 54

6 + 6 + 6 = 18

Hold steady, Croak!

6 + 6 + 6 + 6 = 24

6 + 6 + 6 + 6 + 6 = 30

6 12 18 24 30 36 42 48 54 60

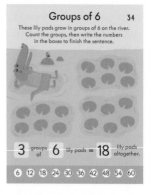

Groups of 6 34
These lily pads grow in groups of 6 on the river. Count the groups, then write the numbers in the boxes to finish the sentence.

3 groups of 6 lily pads = 18 lily pads altogether.

6 12 18 24 30 36 42 48 54 60

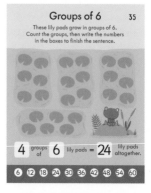

Groups of 6 35
These lily pads grow in groups of 6. Count the groups, then write the numbers in the boxes to finish the sentence.

4 groups of 6 lily pads = 24 lily pads altogether.

6 12 18 24 30 36 42 48 54 60

Flower sixes 36
Help Cheeky count the flowers in sixes. Follow the arrows, and write the new total under each group.

6 → 12 → 18 → 24

48 ← 42 ← 36 ← 30

54 → 60

I know that all of the numbers will be even.

Answers

Honeycomb 37

Find a route across the honeycomb. The next cell's number must always be 6 more than the number of the cell you are on.

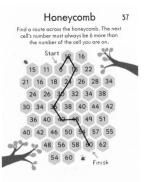

Groups of 6 38

These parrots are perching in groups of 6. Count the groups, then write the numbers in the boxes to finish the sentence.

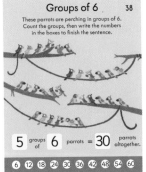

5 groups of 6 parrots = 30 parrots altogether.

6 12 18 24 30 36 42 48 54 60

Groups of 6 39

These parrots are perching in groups of 6. Count the groups, then write the numbers in the boxes to finish the sentence.

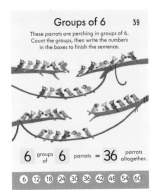

6 groups of 6 parrots = 36 parrots altogether.

6 12 18 24 30 36 42 48 54 60

Sequences 40

Fill in the missing numbers in these sequences so that each number is 6 more than the one before.

6 12 18 24

36 42 48 54

12 18 24 30

24 30 36 42

Groups of 6 41

These leopard cubs all have 6 spots on their fur. Count the cubs, then write the numbers in the boxes to finish the sentence.

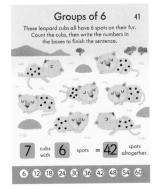

7 cubs with 6 spots = 42 spots altogether.

6 12 18 24 30 36 42 48 54 60

Groups of 6 42

These leopard cubs all have 6 spots. Count the cubs, then write the numbers in the boxes to finish the sentence.

8 cubs with 6 spots = 48 spots altogether.

6 12 18 24 30 36 42 48 54 60

Sequences 43

Fill in the missing numbers in these sequences so that each number is 6 more than the one before.

18 24 30 36

30 36 42 48

6 12 18 24

42 48 54 60

Groups of 6 44

These tiger cubs all have 6 stripes on their fur. Count the cubs, then write the numbers in the boxes to finish the sentence.

9 cubs with 6 stripes = 54 stripes altogether.

6 12 18 24 30 36 42 48 54 60

Groups of 6 45

These tiger cubs all have 6 stripes. Count the cubs, then write the numbers in the boxes to finish the sentence.

10 cubs with 6 stripes = 60 stripes altogether.

6 12 18 24 30 36 42 48 54 60

Answers

6 times table 46

Trace over the dotted numbers and fill in the empty boxes to finish these calculations in the 6 times table.

$1 \times 6 = 6$ $6 \times 6 = 36$

$2 \times 6 = 12$ $7 \times 6 = 42$

$3 \times 6 = 18$ $8 \times 6 = 48$

$4 \times 6 = 24$ $9 \times 6 = 54$

$5 \times 6 = 30$ $10 \times 6 = 60$

Calculation pairs 47

Lep and Baz have been buying party hats. Fill in the numbers in the calculations below to see how many party hats they each have, and to see if Baz is right.

Looks like we both have the same number of party hats, Lep!

Lep's calculation: 6 x rows of 5 = 30

Baz's calculation: 5 x rows of 6 = 30

6 groups 48

These fireflies are in 6 groups. Count how many fireflies are in each group, then write the numbers in the boxes.

$6 \times 2 = 12$

6 12 18 24 30 36 42 48 54 60

6 groups 49

These dragonflies are in 6 groups. Count how many dragonflies are in each group, then write the numbers in the boxes.

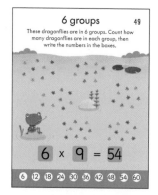

$6 \times 9 = 54$

6 12 18 24 30 36 42 48 54 60

Calculation pairs 50

Fill in the spaces to complete two different calculations for each group of flowers. One has been done for you.

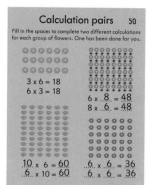

$3 \times 6 = 18$
$6 \times 3 = 18$

$6 \times 8 = 48$
$8 \times 6 = 48$

$10 \times 6 = 60$
$6 \times 10 = 60$

$6 \times 6 = 36$
$6 \times 6 = 36$

Calculation pairs 51

Fill in the spaces to complete two different calculations for each group of flowers. One has been done for you.

$2 \times 6 = 12$
$6 \times 2 = 12$

$5 \times 6 = 30$
$6 \times 5 = 30$

$6 \times 4 = 24$
$4 \times 6 = 24$

$7 \times 6 = 42$
$6 \times 7 = 42$

6 times table 52

Trace over the dotted numbers and fill in the empty boxes to finish these calculations in the 6 times table.

$6 \times 1 = 6$ $6 \times 6 = 36$

$6 \times 2 = 12$ $6 \times 7 = 42$

$6 \times 3 = 18$ $6 \times 8 = 48$

$6 \times 4 = 24$ $6 \times 9 = 54$

$6 \times 5 = 30$ $6 \times 10 = 60$

Calculation match-up 53

Help Lep finish these calculations. Draw a line to join each one to its answer. One has been done for you.

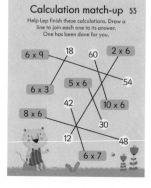

6 x 9   18   60   2 x 6

6 x 3   5 x 6   54

          42   10 x 6

8 x 6   30

          12   48

          6 x 7

How many sixes? 54

Finish these calculations. To help, you could draw around groups of 6 bugs, then count the groups.

$5 \times 6 = 30$
groups of

$7 \times 6 = 42$
groups of

Answers

How many sixes? 55

Finish these calculations. To help, you could draw around groups of 6 berries, then count the groups.

$4 \times 6 = 24$

$8 \times 6 = 48$

Missing numbers 56

Write the missing numbers in the boxes to finish these calculations from the 6 times table.

$7 \times 6 = 42$

$6 \times 2 = 12$

$4 \times 6 = 24$

$6 \times 8 = 48$

$10 \times 6 = 60$

$6 \times 1 = 6$

How many sixes? 57

Finish these calculations. To help, you could draw around groups of 6 fireflies, then count the groups.

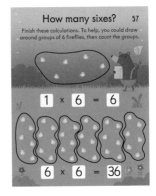

$1 \times 6 = 6$

$6 \times 6 = 36$

How many sixes? 58

Finish these calculations. To help, you could draw around groups of 6 ants, then count the groups.

$3 \times 6 = 18$

$9 \times 6 = 54$

Missing numbers 59

Write the missing numbers in the boxes to finish these calculations from the 6 times table.

$4 \times 6 = 24$

$6 \times 6 = 36$

$8 \times 6 = 48$

$6 \times 3 = 18$

$9 \times 6 = 54$

$6 \times 5 = 30$

Number wheel 60

Help Lep complete the number wheel. Multiply each number with 6 to fill in the empty spaces.

Calculation pairs 61

Help the animals complete these calculations for numbers that are in both the 3 and 6 times tables.

$6 \times 3 = 18$
$3 \times 6 = 18$

$8 \times 3 = 24$
$4 \times 6 = 24$

$3 \times 4 = 12$
$6 \times 2 = 12$

$3 \times 10 = 30$
$6 \times 5 = 30$

$2 \times 3 = 6$
$1 \times 6 = 6$

Calculation match-up 62

Help Froggy finish drawing lines to join each answer to **two** calculations that equal it.

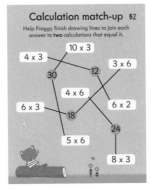

Patterns of 3 and 6 63

Help the mice draw around the numbers from the 3 and 6 times tables.

Answers

Missing numbers 64

Write the missing numbers in the boxes to finish these calculations from the 3 and 6 times tables.

4 x 6 = 24

3 x **5** = 15

9 x 3 = **27**

6 x **6** = 36

7 x 3 = 21

3 x 6 = **18**

Missing numbers 65

Write the missing numbers in the boxes to finish these calculations from the 3 and 6 times tables.

3 x 3 = **9**

6 x **9** = 54

8 x 3 = **24**

6 x **7** = 42

5 x 6 = 30

3 x 4 = **12**

Groups of 4 66

This group of 4 monkeys is having fun around the tree. Trace over the numbers in the boxes to finish the sentence.

1 group of **4** monkeys = **4** monkeys altogether.

4 8 12 16 20 24 28 32 36 40

Groups of 4 67

These groups of 4 bears are paddling their canoes on the river. Count the groups, then write the numbers in the boxes to finish the sentence.

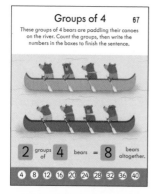

2 groups of **4** bears = **8** bears altogether.

4 8 12 16 20 24 28 32 36 40

Adding in fours 68

Help Lem add up these numbers. Write the totals in the boxes.

4 + 4 + 4 + 4 + 4 + 4 + 4 = **28**

4 + 4 + 4 + 4 + 4 + 4 = **24**

Hold steady, Lez!

4 + 4 = **8**

4 + 4 + 4 = **12**

4 8 12 16 20 24 28 32 36 40

Groups of 4 69

These lily pads grow in groups of 4 on the river. Count the groups, then write the numbers in the boxes to finish the sentence.

3 groups of **4** lily pads = **12** lily pads altogether.

4 8 12 16 20 24 28 32 36 40

Groups of 4 70

These lily pads grow in groups of 4. Count the groups, then write the numbers in the boxes to finish the sentence.

4 groups of **4** lily pads = **16** lily pads altogether.

4 8 12 16 20 24 28 32 36 40

Flower fours 71

Help Tan-tan count the flowers in fours. Follow the arrows, and write the new total under each group.

4 → 8 → 12 → 16

↓

32 ← 28 ← 24 ← 20

I know that all of the numbers will be even.

36 → 40

Honeycomb 72

Find a route across the honeycomb. The next cell's number must always be 4 more than the number of the cell you are on.

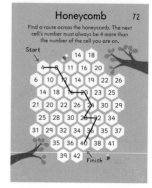

Start

14 18
4→8 11 16 20
6 10 **12** 14 19 22 26
14 18 **16→20** 23 25
21 20 22 **24** 30 29
25 28 30 26 **32** 34
31 29 32 34 **36** 35 37
35 36 **40** 38 41
39 42 Finish

Answers

Groups of 4   73
These parrots are perching in groups of 4. Count the groups, then write the numbers in the boxes to finish the sentence.

5 groups of **4** parrots = **20** parrots altogether.

(4) (8) (12) (16) (20) (24) (28) (32) (36) (40)

Groups of 4   74
These parrots are perching in groups of 4. Count the groups, then write the numbers in the boxes to finish the sentence.

6 groups of **4** parrots = **24** parrots altogether.

(4) (8) (12) (16) (20) (24) (28) (32) (36) (40)

Sequences   75
Fill in the missing numbers in these sequences so that each number is 4 more than the one before.

| 4 | 8 | 12 | 16 |

| 24 | 28 | 32 | 36 |

| 8 | 12 | 16 | 20 |

| 16 | 20 | 24 | 28 |

Groups of 4   76
These leopard cubs all have 4 spots on their fur. Count the cubs, then write the numbers in the boxes to finish the sentence.

7 cubs with **4** spots = **28** spots altogether.

(4) (8) (12) (16) (20) (24) (28) (32) (36) (40)

Groups of 4   77
These leopard cubs all have 4 spots. Count the cubs, then write the numbers in the boxes to finish the sentence.

8 cubs with **4** spots = **32** spots altogether.

(4) (8) (12) (16) (20) (24) (28) (32) (36) (40)

Sequences   78
Fill in the missing numbers in these sequences so that each number is 4 more than the one before.

| 12 | 16 | 20 | 24 |

| 20 | 24 | 28 | 32 |

| 4 | 8 | 12 | 16 |

| 28 | 32 | 36 | 40 |

Groups of 4   79
These tiger cubs all have 4 stripes on their fur. Count the cubs, then write the numbers in the boxes to finish the sentence.

9 cubs with **4** stripes = **36** stripes altogether.

(4) (8) (12) (16) (20) (24) (28) (32) (36) (40)

Groups of 4   80
These tiger cubs all have 4 stripes. Count the cubs, then write the numbers in the boxes to finish the sentence.

10 cubs with **4** stripes = **40** stripes altogether.

(4) (8) (12) (16) (20) (24) (28) (32) (36) (40)

4 times table   81
Trace over the dotted numbers and fill in the empty boxes to finish these calculations in the 4 times table.

$1 \times 4 = 4$ $6 \times 4 = 24$

$2 \times 4 = 8$ $7 \times 4 = 28$

$3 \times 4 = 12$ $8 \times 4 = 32$

$4 \times 4 = 16$ $9 \times 4 = 36$

$5 \times 4 = 20$ $10 \times 4 = 40$

Answers

Calculation pairs 82

Baz and Lep have been growing flowers. Fill in the numbers in the calculations below to see how many flowers they each have, and to see if Baz is right.

Baz's calculation: **4** x rows of **7** = **28**

Lep's calculation: **7** x rows of **4** = **28**

4 groups 83

These flowers are in 4 groups. Count how many flowers are in each group, then write the numbers in the boxes.

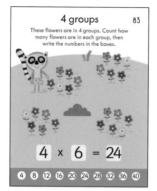

4 x **6** = **24**

④ ⑧ ⑫ ⑯ ⑳ ㉔ ㉘ ㉜ ㊱ ㊵

4 groups 84

These birds are in 4 groups. Count how many birds are in each group, then write the numbers in the boxes.

4 x **8** = **32**

④ ⑧ ⑫ ⑯ ⑳ ㉔ ㉘ ㉜ ㊱ ㊵

Calculation pairs 85

Fill in the spaces to complete two different calculations for each group of fruit. One has been done for you.

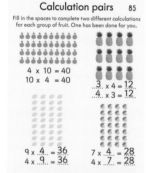

4 x 10 = 40
10 x 4 = 40

3 x 4 = 12
4 x 3 = 12

9 x 4 = 36
4 x 9 = 36

7 x 4 = 28
4 x 7 = 28

Calculation pairs 86

Fill in the spaces to complete two different calculations for each group of bugs. One has been done for you.

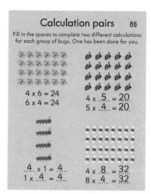

4 x 6 = 24
6 x 4 = 24

5 x 4 = 20
5 x 4 = 20

4 x 1 = 4
1 x 4 = 4

4 x 8 = 32
8 x 4 = 32

4 times table 87

Trace over the dotted numbers and fill in the empty boxes to finish these calculations in the 4 times table.

4 x 1 = 4   4 x 6 = 24

4 x 2 = 8   4 x 7 = 28

4 x 3 = 12   4 x 8 = 32

4 x 4 = 16   4 x 9 = 36

4 x 5 = 20   4 x 10 = 40

Calculation match-up 88

Help Baz finish these calculations. Draw a line to join each one to its answer. One has been done for you.

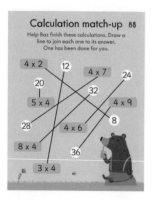

4 x 2   12
         4 x 7
20   24
         32
5 x 4   4 x 9
                8
28   4 x 6
8 x 4   36
3 x 4

How many fours? 89

Finish these calculations. To help, you could draw around groups of 4 bugs, then count the groups.

1 x group of **4** = **4**

4 x groups of **4** = **16**

How many fours? 90

Finish these calculations. To help, you could draw around groups of 4 berries, then count the groups.

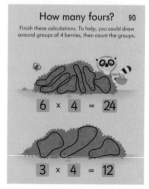

6 x **4** = **24**

3 x **4** = **12**

Answers

Missing numbers   91
Write the missing numbers in the boxes to finish these calculations from the 4 times table.

$1 \times 4 = 4$

$4 \times 7 = 28$

$4 \times 4 = 16$

$4 \times 9 = 36$

$5 \times 4 = 20$

$2 \times 4 = 8$

How many fours?   92
Finish these calculations. To help, you could draw around groups of 4 fireflies, then count the groups.

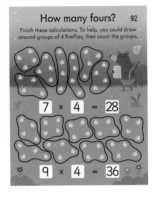

$7 \times 4 = 28$

$9 \times 4 = 36$

How many fours?   93
Finish these calculations. To help, you could draw around groups of 4 ants, then count the groups.

$8 \times 4 = 32$

$2 \times 4 = 8$

Missing numbers   94
Write the missing numbers in the boxes to finish these calculations from the 4 times table.

$3 \times 4 = 12$

$4 \times 5 = 20$

$7 \times 4 = 28$

$4 \times 10 = 40$

$6 \times 4 = 24$

$8 \times 4 = 32$

Number wheel   95
Help Lep complete the number wheel. Multiply each number with 4 to fill in the empty spaces.

Three times four is twelve.

Groups of 8   96
This group of 8 monkeys is having fun around the tree. Trace over the numbers in the boxes to finish the sentence.

1 group of 8 monkeys = 8 monkeys altogether.

8 16 24 32 40 48 56 64 72 80

Groups of 8   97
These groups of 8 bears are paddling their canoes on the river. Count the groups, then write the numbers in the boxes to finish the sentence.

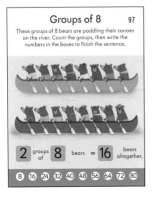

2 groups of 8 bears = 16 bears altogether.

8 16 24 32 40 48 56 64 72 80

Adding in eights   98
Help Lem add up these numbers. Write the totals in the boxes.

$8+8+8+8+8+8+8 = 56$

Hold steady, Baz!

$8+8+8+8 = 32$

$8+8+8+8+8 = 40$

$8+8+8+8+8+8 = 48$

8 16 24 32 40 48 56 64 72 80

Groups of 8   99
These lily pads grow in groups of 8 on the river. Count the groups, then write the numbers in the boxes to finish the sentence.

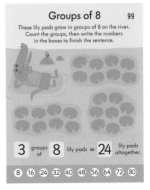

3 groups of 8 lily pads = 24 lily pads altogether.

8 16 24 32 40 48 56 64 72 80

Answers

Groups of 8 100

These lily pads grow in groups of 8. Count the groups, then write the numbers in the boxes to finish the sentence.

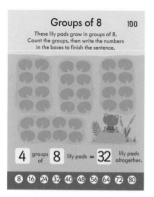

4 groups of **8** lily pads = **32** lily pads altogether.

8 16 24 32 40 48 56 64 72 80

Flower eights 101

Help Tig count the flowers in eights. Follow the arrows, and write the new total under each group.

8 → 16 → 24 → 32
64 ← 56 ← 48 ← 40
72 → 80

I know that all of the numbers will be even.

Honeycomb 102

Find a route across the honeycomb. The next cell's number must always be 8 more than the number of the cell you are on.

Start
26 34
8 14 20 30 38
16 18 22 28 44 46 52
24 26 24 32 48 58
30 32 28 36 54 56 64
38 40 48 56 62 72
44 46 52 66 64 70 76
60 74 72 78 84
68 80
Finish

Groups of 8 103

These parrots are perching in groups of 8. Count the groups, then write the numbers in the boxes to finish the sentence.

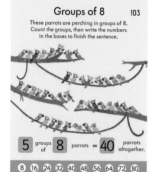

5 groups of **8** parrots = **40** parrots altogether.

8 16 24 32 40 48 56 64 72 80

Groups of 8 104

These parrots are perching in groups of 8. Count the groups, then write the numbers in the boxes to finish the sentence.

6 groups of **8** parrots = **48** parrots altogether.

8 16 24 32 40 48 56 64 72 80

Sequences 105

Fill in the missing numbers in these sequences so that each number is 8 more than the one before.

8 16 24 32
48 56 64 72
16 24 32 40
32 40 48 56

Groups of 8 106

These leopard cubs all have 8 spots on their fur. Count the cubs, then write the numbers in the boxes to finish the sentence.

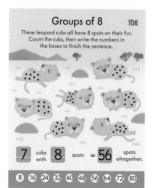

7 cubs with **8** spots = **56** spots altogether.

8 16 24 32 40 48 56 64 72 80

Groups of 8 107

These leopard cubs all have 8 spots. Count the cubs, then write the numbers in the boxes to finish the sentence.

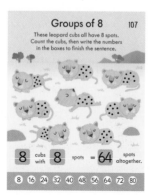

8 cubs with **8** spots = **64** spots altogether.

8 16 24 32 40 48 56 64 72 80

Sequences 108

Fill in the missing numbers in these sequences so that each number is 8 more than the one before.

24 32 40 48
40 48 56 64
8 16 24 32
56 64 72 80

Answers

Groups of 8 — 109

These tiger cubs all have 8 stripes on their fur. Count the cubs, then write the numbers in the boxes to finish the sentence.

9 cubs with **8** stripes = **72** stripes altogether.

8 16 24 32 40 48 56 64 72 80

Groups of 8 — 110

These tiger cubs all have 8 stripes. Count the cubs, then write the numbers in the boxes to finish the sentence.

10 cubs with **8** stripes = **80** stripes altogether.

8 16 24 32 40 48 56 64 72 80

8 times table — 111

Trace over the dotted numbers and fill in the empty boxes to finish these calculations in the 8 times table.

$1 \times 8 = 8$ $6 \times 8 = 48$

$2 \times 8 = 16$ $7 \times 8 = 56$

$3 \times 8 = 24$ $8 \times 8 = 64$

$4 \times 8 = 32$ $9 \times 8 = 72$

$5 \times 8 = 40$ $10 \times 8 = 80$

Calculation pairs — 112

Lep and Baz have been picking mangoes. Fill in the numbers in the calculations below to see how many mangoes they each have, and to see if Baz is right.

Looks like we both have the same number of mangoes, Lep!

Lep's calculation: **8** x rows of **2** = **16**

Baz's calculation: **2** x rows of **8** = **16**

8 groups — 113

These ants are in 8 groups. Count how many ants are in each group, then write the numbers in the boxes.

8 × **5** = **40**

8 16 24 32 40 48 56 64 72 80

8 groups — 114

These butterflies are in 8 groups. Count how many butterflies are in each group, then write the numbers in the boxes.

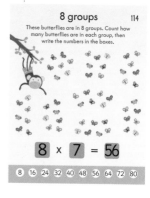

8 × **7** = **56**

8 16 24 32 40 48 56 64 72 80

Calculation pairs — 115

Fill in the spaces to complete two different calculations for each group of objects. One has been done for you.

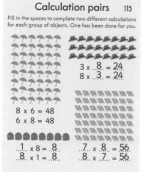

$3 \times 8 = 24$
$8 \times 3 = 24$

$8 \times 6 = 48$
$6 \times 8 = 48$

$1 \times 8 = 8$
$8 \times 1 = 8$

$7 \times 8 = 56$
$8 \times 7 = 56$

Calculation pairs — 116

Fill in the spaces to complete two different calculations for each group of objects. One has been done for you.

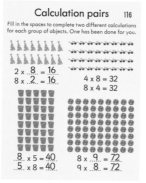

$2 \times 8 = 16$
$8 \times 2 = 16$

$4 \times 8 = 32$
$8 \times 4 = 32$

$8 \times 5 = 40$
$5 \times 8 = 40$

$8 \times 9 = 72$
$9 \times 8 = 72$

8 times table — 117

Trace over the dotted numbers and fill in the empty boxes to finish these calculations in the 8 times table.

$8 \times 1 = 8$ $8 \times 6 = 48$

$8 \times 2 = 16$ $8 \times 7 = 56$

$8 \times 3 = 24$ $8 \times 8 = 64$

$8 \times 4 = 32$ $8 \times 9 = 72$

$8 \times 5 = 40$ $8 \times 10 = 80$

Answers

Calculation match-up 118

Help Ant finish these calculations. Draw a
line to join each one to its answer.
One has been done for you.

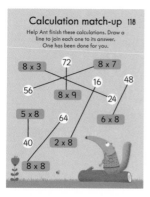

8 x 3 — 72
8 x 7
56
8 x 9 — 16 — 48
24
5 x 8 — 64 — 6 x 8
40 — 2 x 8
8 x 8

How many eights? 119

Finish these calculations. To help, you could draw
around groups of 8 bugs, then count the groups.

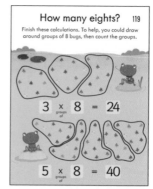

$3 \times 8 = 24$

$5 \times 8 = 40$

How many eights? 120

Finish these calculations. To help, you could draw
around groups of 8 berries, then count the groups.

$7 \times 8 = 56$

$10 \times 8 = 80$

Missing numbers 121

Write the missing numbers in the boxes to finish
these calculations from the 8 times table.

$3 \times 8 = 24$

$8 \times 6 = 48$

$2 \times 8 = 16$

$8 \times 4 = 32$

$7 \times 8 = 56$

$8 \times 10 = 80$

How many eights? 122

Finish these calculations. To help, you could draw
around groups of 8 fireflies, then count the groups.

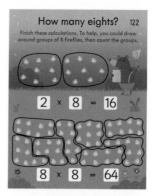

$2 \times 8 = 16$

$8 \times 8 = 64$

How many eights? 123

Finish these calculations. To help, you could draw
around groups of 8 ants, then count the groups.

$4 \times 8 = 32$

$9 \times 8 = 72$

Missing numbers 124

Write the missing numbers in the boxes to finish
these calculations from the 8 times table.

$1 \times 8 = 8$

$8 \times 9 = 72$

$6 \times 8 = 48$

$8 \times 3 = 24$

$5 \times 8 = 40$

$8 \times 8 = 64$

Number wheel 125

Help Lep complete the number wheel. Multiply
each number with 8 to fill in the empty spaces.

8 40
56 1 5 24
7 3
32 4 x8 9 72
6 10
48 8 2 80
64 16

One times eight
is eight.

x8

Calculation pairs 126

Help the animals complete these calculations for
numbers that are in both the 4 and 8 times tables.

$4 \times 4 = 16$
$2 \times 8 = 16$

$4 \times 6 = 24$
$8 \times 3 = 24$

$10 \times 4 = 40$
$5 \times 8 = 40$

$4 \times 8 = 32$
$8 \times 4 = 32$

$2 \times 4 = 8$
$1 \times 8 = 8$

Answers

Calculation match-up 127

Help Lep finish drawing lines to join each answer to two calculations that equal it.

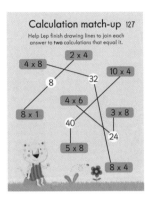

2 x 4
4 x 8
8
32
10 x 4
4 x 6
8 x 1
40
3 x 8
24
5 x 8
8 x 4

Patterns of 4 and 8 128

Help the mice draw around the numbers from the 4 and 8 times tables.

1	2	3	4	5	6	7	8
9	10	11	12	13	14	15	16
17	18	19	20	21	22	23	24
25	26	27	28	29	30	31	32
33	34	35	36	37	38	39	40
41	42	43	44	45	46	47	48
49	50	51	52	53	54	55	56
57	58	59	60	61	62	63	64
65	66	67	68	69	70	71	72
73	74	75	76	77	78	79	80

Help me circle the numbers in the 4 times table.

Can you draw a triangle around each number in the 8 times table for me?

Missing numbers 129

Write the missing numbers in the boxes to finish these calculations from the 4 and 8 times tables.

9 x 4 = 36

8 x 2 = 16

4 x 7 = 28

8 x 10 = 80

6 x 8 = 48

4 x 4 = 16

Missing numbers 130

Write the missing numbers in the boxes to finish these calculations from the 4 and 8 times tables.

4 x 8 = 32

8 x 9 = 72

4 x 5 = 20

8 x 3 = 24

3 x 4 = 12

7 x 8 = 56

Correct calculations 131

Help Tan-tan draw around the calculations in each row that equal the answer at the end. There may be more than one in some rows.

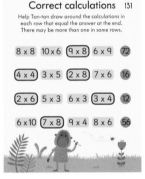

8 x 8   10 x 6   (9 x 8)   6 x 9   72

(4 x 4)   3 x 5   (2 x 8)   7 x 6   16

(2 x 6)   5 x 3   6 x 3   (3 x 4)   12

6 x 10   (7 x 8)   9 x 4   8 x 6   56

Correct calculations 132

Help Tan-tan draw around the calculations in each row that equal the answer at the end. There may be more than one in some rows.

6 x 3   4 x 4   2 x 8   (3 x 5)   15

(9 x 4)   3 x 10   (6 x 6)   5 x 8   36

9 x 8   4 x 7   6 x 10   (8 x 8)   64

(4 x 6)   5 x 8   (6 x 4)   (8 x 3)   24

Mixed tables 133

Write the missing numbers in the boxes to complete these calculations.

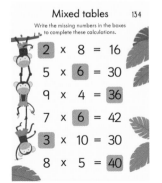

5 x 3 = 15

8 x 4 = 32

9 x 6 = 54

7 x 8 = 56

4 x 10 = 40

3 x 3 = 9

Mixed tables 134

Write the missing numbers in the boxes to complete these calculations.

2 x 8 = 16

5 x 6 = 30

9 x 4 = 36

7 x 6 = 42

3 x 10 = 30

8 x 5 = 40

Mixed tables 135

Write the missing numbers in the boxes to complete these calculations.

3 x 7 = 21

4 x 9 = 36

6 x 6 = 36

3 x 4 = 12

6 x 10 = 60

9 x 8 = 72

Answers

Mixed tables   136

Write the missing numbers in the boxes
to complete these calculations.

4 x 6 = 24

3 x 9 = 27

8 x 6 = 48

4 x 4 = 16

8 x 8 = 64

6 x 3 = 18

Mixed tables   137

Write the missing numbers in the boxes
to complete these calculations.

2 x 3 = 6

8 x 10 = 80

5 x 4 = 20

2 x 4 = 8

8 x 3 = 24

6 x 4 = 24

Mixed tables   138

Write the missing numbers in the boxes
to complete these calculations.

7 x 4 = 28

6 x 8 = 48

3 x 6 = 18

4 x 3 = 12

10 x 6 = 60

8 x 7 = 56